The Case Tractor S

The Company bearing the "Case" name came into being in 1842. J.I. Case was a threshing contractor, and he founded the Company in Rochester, Wisconsin, to make improvements to a "Ground Hog" thresher. By 1844, the Company had moved to Racine, Wisconsin, after an argument with those in power in Rochester who refused to let him use water power for his proposed factory. The move brought the start of manufacture of his own crude threshers, which were gradually improved as new models were built, and by 1848 a thresher complete with horsepower unit cost between $290 and $325.

In 1863, J.I. Case took in 3 partners, Massena Erskine, Robert Baker and Stephen Bull, whilst in 1865, the Eagle trademark was adopted, being modelled after "Old Abe", a magnificent bald eagle that had served in the Civil War as mascot for Company C in the 8th Wisconsin Regiment and was named after President Lincoln. It was not until 1894 that the well known eagle standing on the world made its appearance.

1869 saw the production of the first Case Steam Engine. This was a portable with the cylinders over the firebox and with the crank just behind the chimney. By 1876, 500 traction engines had been produced and an example won a gold medal for excellence at the Centennial Exposition in Philadelphia, and one of the Company's first exports, a thresher, won first prize at the Paris exposition.

In 1880 the Company was reorganized. The partnership was dissolved and the J.I. Case Threshing Machine Company and the J.I. Case Plow Works were incorporated.

In 1884 J.I. Case became involved in an incident that has come to typify the Company's continuing determination to build high quality products. A Case Thresher on a Minnesota farm would not perform to par. Despite efforts of the dealer and then a plant mechanic, the machine refused to function properly. Finally J.I. Case himself travelled the distance to fix the machine that bore his name. Before a large crowd, amazed that the President of the Company would travel all that way, J.I. Case worked on his thresher. It still would not work. Disgusted that such a product had left his factory, he doused it with Kerosene and set it ablaze. The next day, the farmer was presented with a new perfectly operating Case Thresher.

In 1891 J.I. Case died and his brother-in-law Stephen Bull became President and he was replaced by his son Frank K. Bull in 1901.

In 1892, the Company's first I.C. Engined tractor appeared, but it was not until 1895 that ignition and carburetion equipment were developed to a point where production could be contemplated. Several two-cylinder models of differing sizes were produced from this time.

By 1910 Case had entered the Car Market. The Company bought the Pierce Motor Company of Racine, and started to build quality cars in the luxury class, and in 1911 2 racing versions were entered in the first Indianapolis 500 mile race, occupying the pole position and 2 spots on the second row of the grid.

1911 tractor production started in earnest with the 30-60 which was advertised as a "gas traction engine." An example took a Gold Medal in the Winnipeg Plowing Contest, and in 1913 the Clausen Works specializing in tractor production was built, so that by 1916, the new President, Warren J. Davis, headed a Company making a wide variety of traction engines, tractors, cars and farm machinery with bases throughout the world. These were added to in 1919 with the purchase of the Grand Detour Plow Company in Grand Detour, Illinois, to add a line of plows and tillage tools.

Alongside the J.I. Case Threshing Machine Company, there was a separate Company called the J.I. Case Plow Works, whose history demands another volume. At this time the plow works was producing a line of tractors under the name "Wallis." This Company was bought out by Massey Harris in 1928, by which time an agreement was reached that the Threshing Machine Company should continue to carry the name "Case."

Production of traction engines and cars ceased in 1924 with the coming of L.R. Clausen as President.

In 1928 the Company bought out Emmerson Brantingham, one of the pioneer tractor manufacturing Companies, whose influences are seen in the new style tractor range that appeared headed by the "L" the following year.

Early Tractors.

The 30-60 was actually manufactured by the Minneapolis Steel and Machinery Co. of Minneapolis and was produced until 1916. With a twin cylinder engine and crank setting at 360_ the engine gave a power stroke on every revolution.

The next model, the 20-40 had a horizontally opposed twin cylinder engine and was a smaller build, lasting from 1912-20.

The 1913 12.25 was the first tractor designed with the needs of the small farmer in mind and also had a twin cylinder opposed piston engine.

The Cross-Mount range.

The 1915 10-20 showed several 'firsts', including the first 4 cylinder engine and a three wheel configuration. It was the next year which saw the first true cross engined model in the shape of the 9-18.

In 1918 the 10-18 showed design changes to a one-piece cast frame and the reduction in shrouding, whilst the larger 15-27 introduced in the same year followed suit. The 15-27 became the 18-32 in 1925 and lasted until 1928.

The next model in the 'crossmount' range was the 22-40 offered from late 1919 until 1925; unlike the smaller models it featured a steel channel frame, and became the 25-45 in 1925.

The most appealing of the 'crossmounts' was perhaps the 12-20 with its pressed steel wheels which was launched in 1922 and continued until 1930, being renamed the model A in 1928.

The big 40-72 was built from 1923-25 only and its size precluded sales at a time when farming methods were changing.

The C and L models.

The model L was introduced in 1929 and the smaller C the following year. Both tractors were similar in concept, so we will describe them together here in the first instance.

The four cylinder valve in head engines were a rugged development of those fitted to the crossmounts. They featured pressure lubrication and drove the transmission by means of a twin disc over centre clutch. On most other tractors of similar size and design the gearbox shafting runs parallel with the engine crankshaft but, on the new case models, a bevel gear behind the clutch transferred the drive at right angles to the crankshaft, the gearbox shafts being parallel to the rear axle. The final, unique, feature was the use of heavy roller chains to take the drive to the rear axle shafts from the gearbox differential. Three forward and one reverse speed was provided.

Although the basic appearance of the two models remained unchanged over the years, various detail alterations and improvements were made to the tractors. These included better oil pumps, the adoption of vee belt drive to the water pump instead of a flat belt, better carburettors, and the usual changes in magnetos, as the manufacturers improved their products.

Provision eventually came in 1938 for self starting, and this involved some rearrangement of the controls.

Pneumatic typre equipment in the UK was the usual Dunlop or Firestone cast centres on the C, whilst the very size of the wheel equipment on the L saw the use of French & Hecht spoked centres. In the USA, Case fitted their own design of cast centres, with detachable rims - these were, in fact, made by the usual wheel-makers for them.

The Associated Manufacturing Co, were responsible for importing Case tractors into the UK from the early 'thirties, and most export tractors had the tall exhaust and air stacks, whilst domestic US deliveries in the early days ahd been short, angled-down exhausts, and short air stacks.

Braking was provided by the usual, and somewhat inadequate, as far as UK usuage was concerned, external expanding band, acting on a drum, driven from the gearbox countershaft. The first motion shaft provided a convenient power take-off point for the drive pulley.

The CC and CL models

No rowcrop variant on the L was offered, and whereas other manufacturers developed a separate series of "general purpose" or "rowcrop" tractors, the CC rowcrop variant used the same transmission unit. In addition to the normal braking equipment, independent brakes were fitted to the differential shaft.

For domestic US sale, the vee twin or single front wheel was mounted on a swan-necked bracket, attached to the front cover. The rear track was extended by bolting on 12" long extensions to the rear axle shafts, and the mudguards also moved out with the wheel track.

For UK sales however, an adjustable wide axle in the normal position, with a bolt, on outer section on each side, provide adjustment for the track front. By reversing

the stub axles, the clearance was increased, creating the CH model. Extra fendering produced the CO and CV models for orchard and vineyard use, whilst the CI Industrial was available in basic form and as a skid for use in various industrial units.

Crawlers

Case crawler variants were produced in the USA by the Full Track Co, of Milwaukee. In the UK, Roadless Traction produced full track versions of both the C and L models, using their standard and extended variants of their patented rubber jointed tracks. The most famous Case crawlers were those supplied on model L skids to the Royal National Lifeboat Institution. These were fully waterproofed to enable them to go to sea.

Setting the pace in smaller tractors - the R and RC models

Introduced in 1934, the R was specifically designed to cater for the needs of the smaller farmer, or provide a second tractor on a large farm. Coming just after the peak of the depression, Case felt it wise not to spend on developing a new engine for the R and, therefore, took an "off-the-shelf" design from Waukesha.

The gearbox and transmission were a scaled-down version of that fitted to the C.

A rowcrop version was soon marketed: RC was the designation. Early examples had a tall front pillar and worm steering box mounted on the top, with the steering wheel mounted horizontally. Soon, the conventional steering box with drag link was adopted, this allowed the easy fitting of a "wide" front axle.

The R did not undergo the radical re-design of components when Case "streamlined" in 1938-39. A bonnet with more curves and a new radiator top tank sufficed, with the addition of a cast radiator guard in "rising sun".

The bought-in engines were not a contributory factor to the success of the R range, and Case withdrew them in 1940, in readiness for something more reliable.

Styling arrives. The D and DC models.

As with all other products of the American motor industry in the mid-to-late 'thirties, streamlining was fashionable in the tractor industry too! The opportunity was taken to update the range in 1939, and "style" them too. Their grey colour was changed also, to orange.

The first model D and DC tractors bore certain short-lived features. The C style of wheel fixing was retained but the driving position was raised up, necessitationg a less raked steering column. The throttle was moved into the steering column and the dash panel mounted about a third of the way up.

The engine was basically that of the C, but pressure lubrication was extended to the rocker gear. Four forward speeds were now provided. The fuel tank, bonnet, radiator, and grille, were all new. The DC model only varied in that the rear wheel size was larger, and the rowcrop fore carriage added at the front to carry vee twin, single front wheels, or a wide adjustable front axle. This latter was not seen in the UK.

For British sale, the adjustable front axle, used on the CL, was retained.

From 1941, a number of important changes were introduced. The model B reverted to a style lost when the C went out of production. A more shaprply raked steering column, with throttle lever at the base, plus a wide sweeping design of mudguards, were fitted. The latter shared common parts with all D, Do and DV models.

The DC retained the higher driving position, but a new feature was the provision of keyed sliding rear axle shafts, and a new style of mudguard. For UK consumption, the adjustable axle was retained.

In 1942, flange-mounted magnetos became standard, as did alterations to the rear axle shafts and hence the wheels of the DC, and the rationalisation of steering parts, by the fitting of a steering column with universal joint to obtain the shallower rake on the D. The cylinder head was redesigned and raked plugs were now seen. Disc type slewing brakes now graced the DC.

The DEX

This model was peculiar to the United Kingdom and Scandinavia, and was really a "bastard" D, with DC parts. No owners manual was ever produced for this tractor (people not knowing this, still look for such an item). The tractor was basically a C, with the addition of steering brakes in some cases, and the full style of mudguards also used on the DO.

Supply difficulties postwar, plus import tarrifs, meant that the import of Case tractors by the Associated Manufacturers Company ceased in 1949. Spares were supplied for some time after though.

The last D series'

The final series of D and DC tractors never set sail to the United Kingdom, but we mention them here for the benefit of Scandinavian readers. These featured Case's own design of three point, known as "Eagle Hitch". These tractors all featured a higher steering position, LP gas and Cane models were available, and eventually, the engine bore went up to 4". Finally, the twin disc over-centre clutch succumbed in favour of a foot operated single-plate unit, which had been a feature of CI and DI industrials. The D series were replaced by the 400 range in 1955.

"Rolls-Royce" - the big LA

This appeared in 1940 to replace the L. Apart from the restyling exercise carried out, an extra gear in the gearbox, with revised rations, was provided. A number of these machines found their way into the UK under "lease-lend", and after. Many had steel wheels, the resultant postwar conversion to pneumatics providing some interesting dealer-produced wheel centres. Production continued until 1952, when the LA gave way to the similar 500 series, which had a six cylinder engine.

The S and SC

Introduced in 1941, to replace the R, these models had a fourteen year run. A new Case engine was produced for this machine. Neither the standard or rowcrop variants of this model were common in the UK, although some did get in.

1950s Models.

The first model to be redesigned in the 1950s was the LA, which disappeared in favour of a model in similar style but with 6 cylinder diesel, gasoline or LPG engines. The 1953 model was uprated in 1955 to become the 600.

The 400 series replaced the D series in 1955 and inherited that models 'Eagle Hitch' but offered three engine variations and three axle configurations. The smallest models were launched the following year in 1956 as the 300 series.

These models were the last of the old Case tradition. Models from 1957 onward will be covered in a future publication.

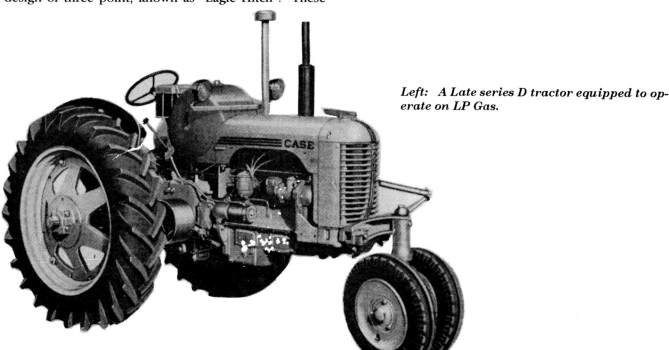

Left: A Late series D tractor equipped to operate on LP Gas.

1892 Case (Patterson)

Case were one of the first traction engine manufacturers to experiment in the internal combustion power field. This experimental tractor was completed in 1892 and powered by a twin cylinder engine to the design of William Paterson, on what was essentially steam engine running gear, with a sliding key used to engage the single forward and reverse gear. The engine rated at approximately 16/20 hp is of interest as it shows a different approach to that which became the norm.

The large tank at the front end of the tractor is the carburettor. The petrol was atomized by having air drawn through it to pick up vapour before entering the engine.

The engine was a twin cylinder horizontal type in which a single throw crankshaft connected directly to the piston in the open end of the rear cylinder via a connecting rod and the far piston (with the cylinder opening in the opposite direction) through pitman rocker arm and a short connecting rod. Whilst the ignition was effected by the make and break of a bolt in the piston head contacting a stationary insulated electrode on the compression stroke, with the spark therefore occurring just after top dead centre on the outward stroke.

The fate of this tractor is unknown but the complexities of its ignition and carburetion must have held Case back for some time before re-entering the IC tractor business.

1910. 31/60 Experimental Model.

It took Case 18 years before this next experiment. In November, 1910, the company demonstrated a 30/60 hp model, which in revamped form, was put into production as tests proved very satisfactory. It shared wheels and some other parts with the companies steam products, whilst the engine was from the Twin City company.

1912 - 16. 30/60 Model

By 1912, the 30/60 was ready for production, manufacture being sub-contracted to the Minneapolis Steel and Machinery Company of Minneapolis, Minnesota, otherwise known as Twin-City. It remained virtually unchanged throughout its production, although by May, 1914 it was producing 75 hp. As the cranks were 360 degrees apart, the engine gave a power stroke every revolution. The short comings of the design were the balancing of the 2-10" pistons leading in the same direction, and keeping the two igniters of the make-and-break ignition in time.

1912 - 1920. The 20/40.
Learning all the time, the Company followed the 30/60 with a smaller tractor, the 20/40. So successful was this design that it remained in production right through to 1920. To avoid the out of balance forces of the earlier tractor this model was fitted with a horizontally opposed twin Cylinder engine, which was naturally balanced. So economical was it that it won 2 Gold Medals for fuel economy at the Winnipeg Contest.

1913-1918. The Case 12/25.
Introduced in 1913, this tractor was the first tractor designed for the needs of the smaller farmer, the earlier large models were better suited to large farms and ranches.

1915 - 1920 Case 10/20.
The 10/20, which came into production in 1915, brought several 'firsts' to the Case range.
It was their production tractor to use a four cylinder engine, and it was their first three wheeler. Three wheeled tractors were very much in vogue in 1915, with the right hand rear following the path of the front. However, unlike the Bull tractor, the Case tractor left rear wheel could be brought into engagement with a jaw clutch, when pulling to give added traction. It was capable of a 23 foot turning circle, whilst the brake stopped the belt pulley and when in gear stopped the forward motion of the tractor.

1916 - 1918. Case 9/18.
This tractor, which was demonstrated during 1916, became available toward the end of the year. It was the first of the true cross engined Case tractors with its transverse 4 cylinder engine, a feature which stayed with the Case line through to 1929. This lightweight tractor was aimed as a direct competitor to Wallis and International Harvester. This model provided a streamlined appearance, and together with the bold lettering and coachlining is a far cry from the earlier production types. One of these tractors won first prize in the up to 24 horsepower class in the 1920 Lincoln Trials, and is the earliest Case type shown to have been imported into the UK in period.

1922 Case 10/18 (above)
Introduced in 1918, the 10/18 showed a change of emphasis in the Case range, gone is most of the fancy bodywork to be replaced with a rugged, more spartan look. The built-up chassis frame has been replaced by a one-piece cast-iron frame. The UK price in 1920 was £375.

1918-1924 Case 15/27. Below is seen the second of the cast frame tractors, this tractor was introduced in November 1918. It featured a water type air cleaner, which although requiring constant attention, was certainly better than the 'instant rebore kit' of nothing at all.

Above: -Left hand side of the 15/27 showing the dog for attaching the starting handle and the small petrol tank starting.

Above right: Rear view showing the high ground clearance and swinging draw-bar together with a myriad of controls.

Right: "Aeroplane" view of the 15/27 showing the typical layout of the crossmount tractors. The 22/40 differed in as much as each rear wheel was independently powered by its own spur gear from the transverse shaft below the steering box.

Left: An 18/32 showing optional metal cleats.

Rerated as the 18/32 model K in January 1925. The tractor remained in production until 1928. Modifications included wide belt pulley, tall intake stack, and engine running to 1,000 r.p.m. instead of 900.

Above: Rubber cleats on disc type wheels for avoiding damage to road surfaces are shown on this tractor.

Left: Left-hand view of the standard model with lugs on the rear wheels

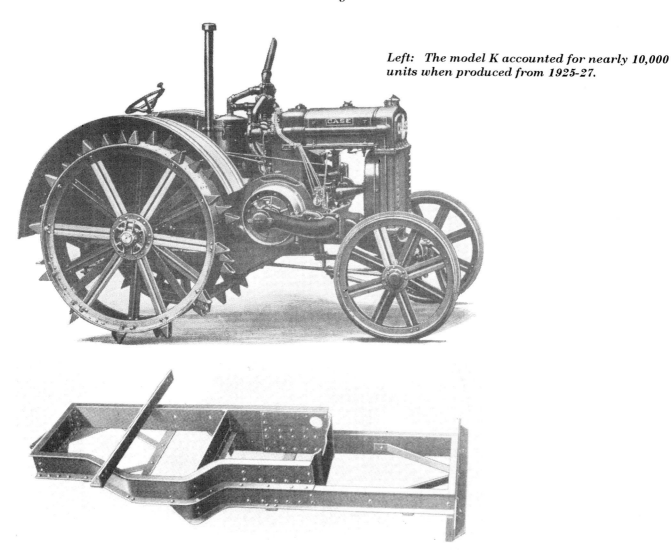

Left: The model K accounted for nearly 10,000 units when produced from 1925-27.

Below: 1919 - 1925 - 22/40. First offered in late 1919, this tractor differed from the smaller sizes in that its frame was built up from channel iron and boiler plate as seen above, , stating that this was the strongest possible construction for a frame of this size. 1920's technology could not guarantee satisfactory casting of a one piece unit of such a size.

Right: like the 15/27 the 22/40 was uprated to the 25/45 in 1925 and remained in production to 1929. This was a very big tractor giving tremendous power and yet remained viable for farmwork.

Left: flywheel side of the 25/45. Only just over 1100 units were built from 1925-7.

Right: The 25/45 power unit, as those of the smaller tractors in the range was available as a skid unit for industrial and other applications. To all intents and purposes these were tractors without transmission and wheels and inherited the characteristics of its wheeled brethren.

1922 - 1928 - model 12/20
1928 - 1930 - model A
Perhaps the most appealing of the crossmount range was the 12/20. A notable feature of these tractors is the pressed steel wheels in which the spokes and felloes were cut out of one piece of 3/16 " steel plate, which were riveted to 5/16 " steel tyres in the drive wheels and 3/16 " on the fronts. Two other views of the tractor are shown left and below. Nearly 12000 of this model were built under its two designations.

Right: The driving position of the 12/20. Considerable attention was taken in the finish of the tractors with lined out fenders and lettering

Below: The 12/20 cylinder block with its replaceable liners was to a general design to be found on Case tractors until the 1950s.

Below: The largest of the crossmounts was produced from 1923-1925, and was rated at 40/72. This mammoth of a tractor weighed in at 9 1/2 tons.
Like many of the other giants of the period, its job was finished when the prairies were conquered and was a victim of the new style of farming caused by the rowcrop revolution, it certainly was big and powerful. It had a 4 cylinder engine with the cylinders cast in pairs, of 7" bore and 8" stroke, 20.41 litres. The Nebraska test showed 49.87 hp at the drawbar and no less than 91hp at the belt pulley. This meant that a maximum drawbar pull of 10680 lbs was available, whilst it had an exceptionally high belt pulley speed allowing 3827 feet per minute at normal engine speed. The 1923 price for this tractor was $4900.

The 12/20 was one of the first tractors to be sold in specialised forms for specific uses. The Orchard version with its redesigned exhaust and fewer projections differed little from standard, (above) but the industrial version (below) was a very different arrival. Fitted with solid rubber tyres all round, no fenders, low exhaust and purposeful looking bumper, it was well adapted to meet its new role.

Right: An early L on steel wheels. The design was extremely well executed and came to Britain in 1930, when it would have cost £348.

Left: British L tractors usually had locally cast front and rear wheel centres, as seen here, but note the original Case front hub nut.

Right: This L, sold in America, features wheels with pressed steel rims clipped to cast centres. Note also the short exhaust fitted for domestic US consumption.

Left: Another design of `Case' centre is seen on this L - the tyres are by Goodyear.

Right: Another tractor from the opposite side. Note the rear wheel weights and magneto guard. When tested at Nebraska, in 1938, the result was 32-45hp, with a maximum drawbar pull of 3635lbs, whilst the tractor itself weighed 8025lbs on rubbers and 5300lbs on steels.

Above: An L, fitted with optional accessories; bonnet sides, enclosed cab, electrical equipment and remote air cleaner (left view only). The cab was advertised as protecting the operator in all kinds of weather. Windows and doors were removable, as was the whole outfit. The power unit of the L was reliable and smooth running, and this made the tractor very popular with threshermen.

Large
Steering Wheel.

Irreversible
Gears

Removable
Cylinder Sleeves.

Efficient
Valve-in-head
Engine.

High Tension
Magneto.

Fly-Ball
Governor-Adjustable.

Big Fuel Tank.

Hardened Roller
Chain Drive.

Tubular
Radiator
Rigidly
Mounted.

Upright
Crank.

Swinging
Drawbar.

Smooth
Acting
Clutch.

3-Bearing Crankshaft
Drilled for Pressure
Lubrication.

Geared Type
Oil Pump.

Steel Gears Drop Forged,
Machine Cut and Hardened.

Pressure Lubrication
to Connecting Rod and
Camshaft Bearings.

Top: The Case L in section showing the simplicity of design and the roller chain drive to the rear axle. Although simple in concept, the provision of pressure lubrication in the engine coupled with an overhead valve layout put this tractor ahead of much of the competition, expressly the Fordson.   The bevel gears at the rear of the clutch, and the transverse intermediate shafting in the gearbox were to be a feature of Case tractors until the mid 1950s.

Above: The L engine , indicating the position of the head sheild and showing the unique 'Case' cast iron air cleaner assembly in unit with the manifold.   Early tractors also featured a flat fan belt, whilst the last in 1938 were equipped to take self starters.

The complete model revolution at Case in 1929 came following the Emerson Brantingham takeover and out went the yeavy cross-engined tractors.   The conventional models which replaced them were very well designed and the L just described was the first model to be introduced, with a claimed rating of 26/40HP. The L was available in Britain by 1930 and cost £348, taking part in the tractor trials of that year, and the model was subsequently demonstrated throughout the country along with a Roadless tracked example and an early model C. (opposite page bottom).   When tested in Nebraska in 1938 the result was 32-42HP at belt and drawbar with a maximum drawbar pull of 3635 lbs., whilst the tractor itself weighed in at 8025lbs on rubbers and 5300lbs on steels.

Right: An industrial model LI was also offered and the basic model is seen here.

Left: Various options were available to industrial users, such as the lighting set, twin rear wheels, and sprung axle seen here.

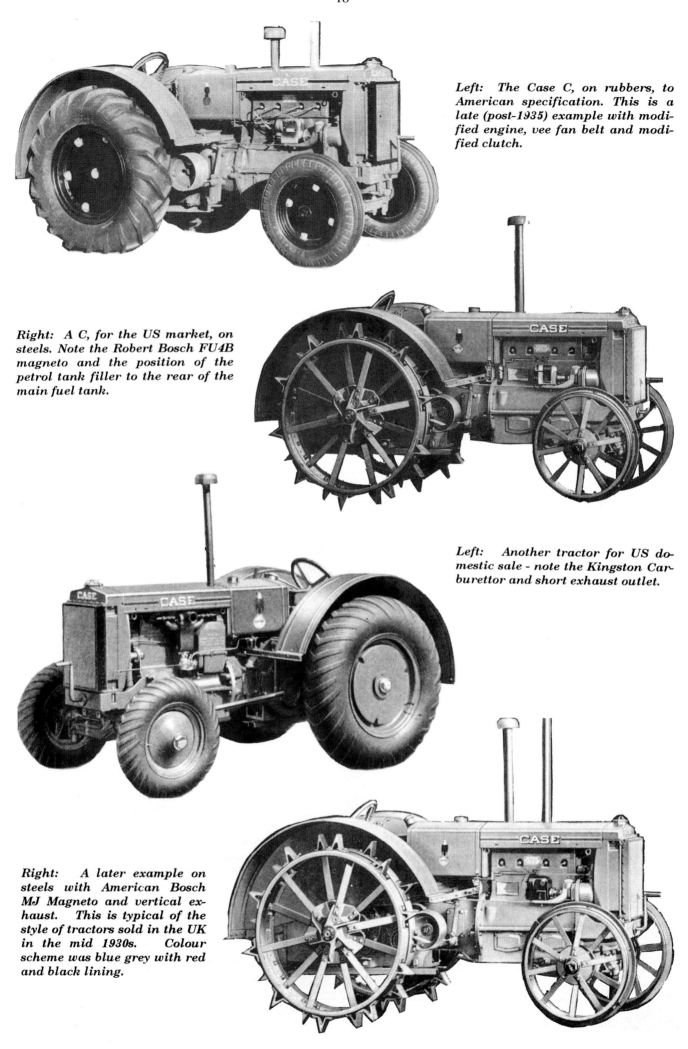

Left: The Case C, on rubbers, to American specification. This is a late (post-1935) example with modified engine, vee fan belt and modified clutch.

Right: A C, for the US market, on steels. Note the Robert Bosch FU4B magneto and the position of the petrol tank filler to the rear of the main fuel tank.

Left: Another tractor for US domestic sale - note the Kingston Carburettor and short exhaust outlet.

Right: A later example on steels with American Bosch MJ Magneto and vertical exhaust. This is typical of the style of tractors sold in the UK in the mid 1930s. Colour scheme was blue grey with red and black lining.

The model C was introduced in 1930 as the small sister of the L range. It was very much a scaled-down version of its big brother but its size allowed its conversion for other specialised uses. Industrial and orchard tractors had already been offered with the cross-engined 12-20 but the row-crop dimension was added with the CC.

Right: To demonstrate the reliability of the C, Northumberland dealer James E. Reed of Shiremoor placed a C on extended 3 day test at Cockle Park, Northumberland. James Reed is seen on the left of this photograph along with local farmers.

Left: The CO variant is seen here. The provision of a downturned exhaust outlet, plus the enclosed fenders to prevent overhanging citrus branches from coming into contact with the rear wheels, are the main differences from standard.

Right: The CI industrial model in basic form.

Left: The CC on steels. The rear axle could be extended using 12" bolt on sections, and the mudguards moved out to suit the track. A 12" extension is in place on the rear wheels of this example.

Right: : A later CC, with single row rear wheels and Bosch MJ magneto.

Left: A CC, at work in the UK. Note the starting handle position. This tractor was registered in Bedfordshire in 1937.

Right: The CC, on rubbers. When the Ford Motor Co. were developing their rowcrop model 'N' for the US market one of these tractors was acquired and the similarities in axle and steering layout are noteworthy.

Left: The CH. These tractors were CC fitted with standard type front axle, with the stub axles inverted to give higher ground clearance.

Right: A CL, with adjustable front axle for the UK market, hauling a Case pick-up baler. This is being driven from the tractor PTO. This model was a crossbred C and CC (q.v.).

Left: A CL at work with a steerage hoe. Note the Dunlop pneumatic cast centres fitted to this model sold in England. Adjustable front axles rather than vee twin formation were far more popular in the United Kingdom as most tractors had to cope with a variety of work including some tasks where increased stability was essential.

Left: The model R is seen here in its original grey, unstyled form, For the first time, for Case, a cylindrical aircleaner was adopted. Introduced in 1934 to cater for the needs of the smaller farmer, the R would also fulfill the role of a second tractor on a larger farm. It was unique in being powered by a Waukesha side valve engine rather than Case's own, and was most suited for the lighter jobs in order to keep costs down.

Right: The R in its orange, styled 'rising sun' form. This exercise was not as comprehensive a one as applied to the C and L models as the styling on this model always looked like an afterthought.

Left: This styled R shows clearly the Continental engine features. These are all models for the US market, most UK examples had contemporary British-made cast wheel centres.

Left: The original RC featured a tall front pillar with the steering box on top .

Right: A later model, with conventional steering arrangements, is seen here.

Left: A styled version, complete with full electrical system. The RC was the first Case model to introduce the sliding axle system of rowcrop rear wheel spacing, rather than the cumbersome `add-on' axle system, used on the CC and early DCs.

Left: A view of an early D, from serial 4300701, showing the radical changes in driving position and styling from previous models. By now, Case were using their own magnetos, but the carburretion equipment was by Zenith.

Right: An extra speed in the gearbox made the tractor more versatile, especially when rubbers were fitted. The type of centres, fitted here, were usually seen only in the USA. British examples often had cast Dunlop centres.

Left: The DEX was a model created specifically for the UK market, and a typical example is shown here, complete with Dunlop wheel centres. The low driving position was almost like driving a Fordson, and it has been suggested that this was requested by the War Agricultural committees. Unlike Fordson, Case continued to paint their tractors in Flambeau red.

Left: The later D reverted to the model C look, with its squat stance and sweeping mudguards. When the flange mounted magneto was adopted, the dynamo was resited and driven direct form the fan belt. The example illustrated here was for Scandinavia, as it has a petrol manifold and lighting equipment on the fenders.

Two DO tractors, the lower one equipped for LP gas operation. The vaporiser was plumbed into the tractor's cooling system, to turn the liquid gas into vapour, which can be clearly seen, below. The later flange mounted magneto can be seen on the example, right.

Left: A postwar DC3 tractor, with full electrics and flange mounted magneto. From tractor 4511449, a series of changes had started and the splined rear axle shafts and revised cylinder head layout, using 18mm plugs, inclined down into the combustion chambers instead of being horizontal.

The early DC4 was very similar to the D, but for UK consumption used the front axle of the Cl and rear axle of the CC, to give track adjustment. Note the Robert Bosch magneto and unusual front wheels on the steel-wheeled example to the right. Below is a pneumatic tyred version, and bottom right can be seen the front axle in close-up. This also gives a good view of the radiator grille.

Above: A superb view of an early DC4 at work, with a steerage hoe .

Right: A DEX, fitted with Roadless DG4 driven girder half tracks. Note the position of the headlamps, for UK sale, and the cast front wheel centres.

Below: A DEX, equipped with Roadless   rubber-jointed   half tracks. The Case magneto, dynamo and light positions on UK-imported models can clearly be seen. These tractors were, in the main, supplied to the RAF.

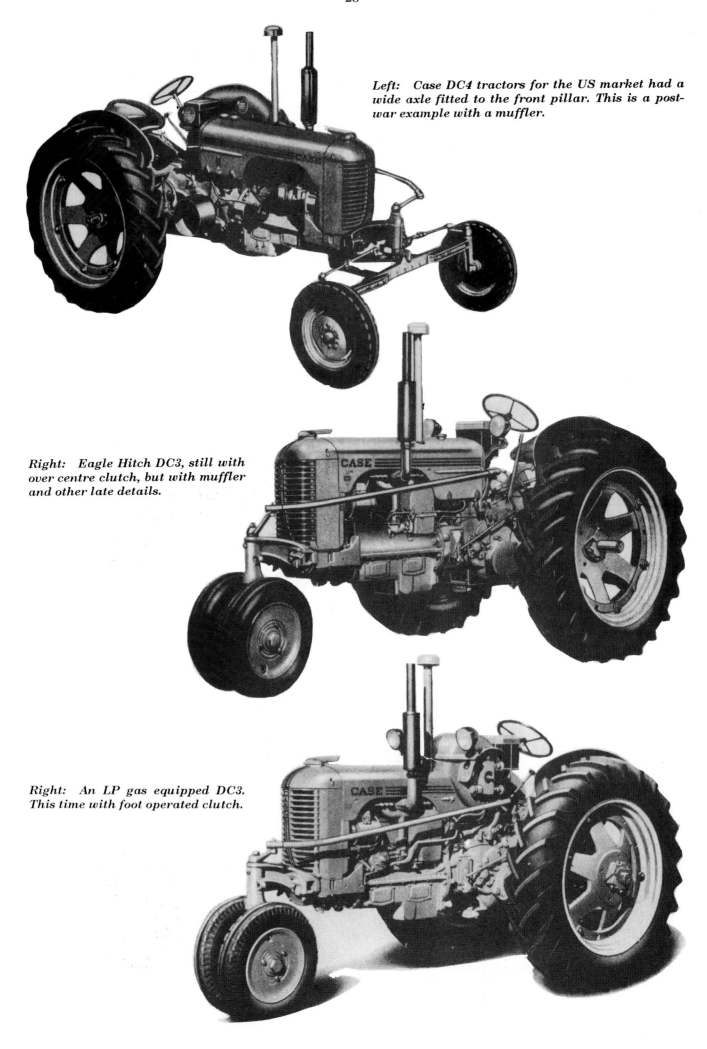

Left: Case DC4 tractors for the US market had a wide axle fitted to the front pillar. This is a post-war example with a muffler.

Right: Eagle Hitch DC3, still with over centre clutch, but with muffler and other late details.

Right: An LP gas equipped DC3. This time with foot operated clutch.

Left: A late (1954) example of a D, with Eagle Hitch. This tractor is an export model. Note the return of the more upright steering position because of the lift.

Right: A late DC4, with Eagle Hitch. Note the external oil filter on the engine block.

Left: A DS Cane tractor. The drive to the rear wheels was, of course, by roller chain.

Right: The 1941 introduction of the S range of tractors eliminated the less than popular R from the range. It ran until 1955, and used Case's own engine. A late model is shown here.

Right: The SC, fitted with a wide front axle. Surprisingly, both RC and SC tractors reached the UK with this axle.

Left: The SO, with citrus fenders.

Right: A late SC3, showing muffler, petrol manifold and footboards.

The VA series of tractors. Above, a standard model; below right, a VAN, with wide front axle; and below, left, a VAO orchard model.

No book on Case would be complete without a look at the most famous of all Case models, the LA.

Left: An LA, on steel wheels, is typical of such machines imported into the UK. Apart from the various styling changes, including colour, the LA differed from the L in having an extra forward speed.

Right: A pneumatic tyred example is seen here with authentic Case centres. Because of the tyre sizes, such pneumatic tyres examples, as were imported, had Case own centres. Many tractors in the UK seem to have postwar centres fitted when the steel wheels were replaced by pneumatics. These are from various sources.

Left: A Ricefield LA typifies late production and, in addition, has oversize rear tyres, petrol manifold, silencer and lighting equipment.

Above Left: : The footplate of the LA, showing the large amount of space available to the operator, or for the fitting of a winch. Note also, the swinging drawbar, articulated gearstick and position of the battery box and toolbox. Early tractors had a wooden floor, later ones, chequer plate.

Above Right: Another late LA with self-starting equipment and lights

Left: An LA equipped for LP gas operation. The so-called 'light ends' of the petroleum refining process had been successfully contained by storage under pressure from the 1930s and the use of Butane or Propane as road fuels was actively pursued in the USA. Most tractor manufacturers were also offering LP gas powered units by the early 1950s.

Left: Offered from 1947, with LP gas equipment, the arrangements for this fuel can be seen here.

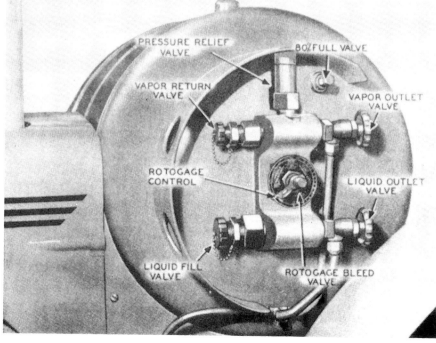

Right: The Model 410 standard tractor. The 400 series was introduced in 1955 as a logical progression from the D series, and featured the Eagle Hitch, Case's own tractor mounted hydraulic three point linkage first seen on the earlier model some years previously. It was available in various axle configurations and 3 engine variations, the spark ignition gasoline engine is fitted here.

Right: Model 410 standard tractor equipped with Eagle Hitch. The Eagle hitch had appeared first on late D series tractors and in concept it followed the Ferguson three point linkage but with no draft control and quick release couplings on the lower arms. Conversion arms were later offered so that standard linkage equipped tools could be utilised.

Left: Model 411 three wheel tractor fitted with single front wheel. Note the sliding hub rear wheel configuration.

Above and right: - Model 411 general purpose 4 wheeled tractor with wide front axle. The 400 series replaced the D but had an engine which ran at higher revs.

Left: Model 411 general purpose tractor with vee twin front wheels and seed drill.

Left: Smallest of the new range was the model 300, introduced in 1956, shown in rowcrop form here. A choice of Case petrol or Continental diesel engines were offered and the model was also available in enhanced form as the 350 series with more powerful engines and transmission options.

Right: This range exemplified by a standard or Utility model here, is fitted with theEagle-Hitch and shows the driver sitting further forward on the tractor, like the 400 the driver is seated over and in front of the axle, giving improved forward vision without having to tower over the tractor bonnet.

COLOUR OF CASE TRACTORS

Whilst numerous examples of Orange Case Tractors have now been well restored in this country, and the correct Flambeau orange is readily available, this is not the situation with the earlier grey tractors. The following is again an extract of a letter from Case themselves to an American enthusiast.

"Model 'L' tractors were painted grey with red wheels, spokes and rims. The grey paint is currently available under J.I. Case part No. B13017 (qt); red Case part No. B13010 (qt). The raised ribs bordering the fenders employed a red stripe approximately 3/16" wide with a narrower 1/8" white stripe over the red. The Case logo cast into the radiatorlgrille shroud was painted silver.

Although it is not mentioned above, a similar stripe to the mudguards appears on the
bonnet sides at either end of the Case logo which is again painted silver.

DATING OF CASE TRACTORS

Over the years, many conflicting reports have been written as to the Dating of Case tractors. The following is based on a letter from Case themselves:-

According to our records, your Case Model 'L' tractor, serial number L4207073 was manufactured in 1938.

The year of manufacture on tractors employing a 6 digit serial number may be determined by subtracting 3 from the first and fourth digit. E.g. L 321375 - 33-3 = (19)30 whilst for units after 1938 employing 7 digit serial numbers, which began with 1939 production, subtracting 4 from the first 2 digits provides the year of manufacture.

1953 saw the start of another 'all change' at Case. The first model out was the 500 available in diesel, gasoline or L.P. gas versions. This was a big standard tread tractor bearing more than a passing resemblance to the L.A. The Nebraska test showed drawbar horsepower of 56/32. By this time, electric starting and lighting equipment were standard features.

The 500 also saw the colour change to Desert Sand, a sort of yellowy ochre, two toned with the old flambeau Red.

The biggest tractor of the new range was introduced in 1955. The model 600 was available with all the usual engine options, and is shown in diesel form, above, and L.P. gas form below. The tractor was an uprated 500 in effect.

LP gas equipped tractors were offered by most US manufacturers in the 1950s and the Case 600 was one of the largest. LP gas burns more cleanly than petrol/gasoline and does not contaminate the lubricating oil, but valve seats and heads have to be specially hardened due to the higher exhaust temperatures encountered.

Three conversions, by Roadless Traction, of C units to full tracks.
Left: A standard model with original type of side frames.

Right: A special model with high ground clearance and long tracks for forestry work.

Left: An extended model, complete with canopy and lighting. Note that all these examples have the German Bosch FU4B magneto, and the interposition of the generator between the magneto and the timing drive when electrics were fitted. Roadless provided special new rear axle housings, with the steering brakes enclosed for these conversions, and steering was by a normal wheel.

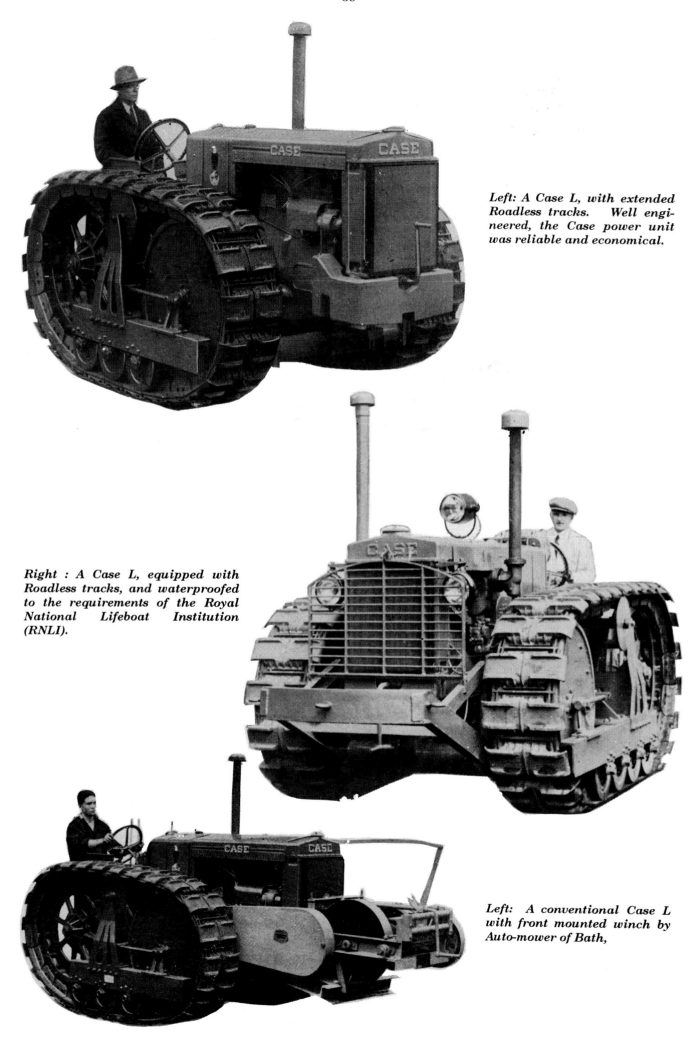

Left: A Case L, with extended Roadless tracks. Well engineered, the Case power unit was reliable and economical.

Right : A Case L, equipped with Roadless tracks, and waterproofed to the requirements of the Royal National Lifeboat Institution (RNLI).

Left: A conventional Case L with front mounted winch by Auto-mower of Bath,

Three shots of a Case L, with Roadless tracks, but with a difference. The engine is a Hesselmann design diesel fuel engine, with which Case experimented for a short time in the late thirties. This incorporated fuel injection, but retained a low compression ratio, relying on spark ignition to ignite the fuel. Petrol was used for the first two or three minutes and then the fuel pump rack opened and burning of diesel fuel started.

Left: A side view of the Case RNLI tractor showing the aluminium cover over the engine to protect the ignition components. All inlets had to be equipped with watertight seals, and all engine and transmission systems were linked up to the engine air intake pipe.

Right: The other side of the RNLI conversion. Even the carburettor had to be assembled using special sealant. The governor was enclosed in a completely waterproof casing. All electrical items were also fully waterproofed, as it was necessary to start the tractor when sometimes, fully submerged.

Below: A Roadless-equipped L mole ploughing.

This page: Three views of lifeboats being launched by late example Roadless conversions based on the LA. The top and centre pictures show the Cullercoats lifeboat with an unknown tractor in use.

KLA84, number T50 winiching in the New-biggin lifeboat. This tractor was new to that station in July 1949 and remained there for ten years.

Left: A rear view of the LA conversion showing the Capstan winch fitted, and the 'bridge'

Right: A front view of a lifeboat tractor, now based on the Case LA. This was T39 which was a relief unit from 1947 when new to 1948, then spent the next nine years at New Quay in Cardiganshire, and from 1957-64 was based at Minehead.

Each tractor was submerged in a tank at the Roadless factory and tested for 24-hours.

Left: The lifeboat dwarfs the tractor which can just be seen to the rear. This scene is at North Sunderland and the tractor T37 was based there from 1954-61.

Above and left: The Case LA fitted with Roadless DG4 driven girder type half-tracks.

Below: Case DEX with Roadless tracks as fitted with hand operated crane for use by the RAF.

Left: The model C engine. Basically unchanged through Cs production, provision for starter motor was added at the rear of this side of the block from 1938, whilst the base mounted magneto and horizontal plug head, carried on into D production.

Right: Spare parts for Case tractors were none to easy to come by during the war, and as import tarriffs bit in the late 1940s and early 1950s so too did the supply of tractors dry up. This is a wartime modification by dealers Reeds of Shiremoor who fabricated a bracket to allow the use of a BTH magneto. Note also the inciined plugs on this later engine.

Below: A splendid view of an early D at work 'somewhere in England' with a Case pickup baler.

Above: The C at the Northumberland County Show 1935 alongside a little known competitor!

Left: That enamel sign-board must be a collectors piece in its own right.

Right: The Case fleet at Hartley Mains Farm, Northumberland, England. There are 2 x Cs, 2 CIs and an early DC4 but the tractor in the centre has a non-standard axle.

Right: For threshing and timber hauling work, a winch could be fitted neatly at the rear, driven from the standard power take off shaft.

Left: A becabbed late tractor draws a crowd at a ploughing demonstration.

Below: A scene from the 1960s with preserved Case LA and Oliver 90 tractors ploughing in Northumberland.

CASE TRACTORS – 1910–1930

Model Type Number	30.60	20.40	12.25	10.20	9.18	10.18	12.20	15.27	22.40	40.72
Rated BHP Drawbar/belt	30.60	20.40	12.25	10.20	9.18	10.18	12.20	15.27	22.40	40.72
Engine RPM	365	475	675	800	900	1050	1050	900	850	750
Speeds MPH		2, 3	1.75, 2.2	2¼	2¼, 3½	2¼, 3½	2.23	2¼, 3 mph	2.2, 3.2	2.07, 2.97
Capacity Cubic Inches						236	267.3	381.7	641	1230
14" pbW Ord. Conditions	7–8	5–6	4	3	2	2	3	4	4	8–12
Tractor Length			149"	158"	123"		109"	127"	153"	200"
Width			78"	67"	58"		58.5/6"	72"	82½"	105"
Height without Exhaust Pipe			76"	60"	61"		55½"	68"	90"	110"
Wheel Base							65"	76½"	96"	129"
Weight		13780 lbs.	8995 lbs.	5080 lbs.	3770 lbs.	3400 lbs.	4230 lbs.	6350 lbs.	9200 lbs.	21200 lbs.
Turning Circle		41 ft.		23 ft.		22 ft.	24 ft.	27¼ ft.	40½ ft.	36¾ ft.
Price	$2800	$2030 (1914) $2500 (1920)	$1650 (1918) $1350 (1913)	$1025	$900	£375 UK	$1095	$1800 £475 UK	$3100	$4900
Engine:										
Cylinders	2 side by side	2 opp.	2 opp.	4 vert.	4	4	4	4	4	4
Bore	10"	8¾"	7"	4¼"	3.7/8"	3.7/8"	4.1/8"	4½"	5½"	7"
Stroke	12"	9"	7"	6"	5"	5"	5"	6"	6¾"	8"
Engine Lubrication	← Maddison Kipp force sight pressure feed and Splash →						Pressure	← Pressure feed through drilled crankshaft →		
Ignition	← KW →		←			→ Kingston Magneto	HT Berling Magneto	HT Magneto		
Air Cleaner	← NO AIR CLEANERS →						Water	Water	Water	Water
Carburetor	←					→	Kingston →			
Cooling System	←	induced draught	← pump radiator & fan →			→	Copper tube & fan type with cast iron frame			
Chassis Frame	←		fabricated steel			→	cast iron single iron casting		8" channel fabricated steel	8" & 10" steel fabrication

Above: This is the way many Case tractors came into the United Kingdom - Cased! The picture shows a DC4 model before unpacking begins.